Skills Builders

Grammar and Punctuation

YEAR 5

Maddy Barnes

RISING STARS

Rising Stars UK Ltd, 7 Hatchers Mews, Bermondsey Street, London SE1 3GS
www.risingstars-uk.com

Every effort has been made to trace copyright holders and obtain their permission for the use of copyright materials. The publishers will gladly receive information enabling them to rectify any error or omission in subsequent editions.

All facts are correct at time of going to press.

Published 2013
Reprinted 2013
Text, design and layout © 2013 Rising Stars UK Ltd

Project manager: Dawn Booth
Editorial: Sue Walton
Proofreader: Margaret Crowther
Design: Words & Pictures Ltd, London
Cover design: Amina Dudhia
Acknowledgements: p.11 iStock/kysa; p.12 iStock/Scott Wilson;
p.24 iStock/Cyro Pintos

British Library Cataloguing-in-Publication Data
A CIP record for this book is available from the British Library.

ISBN: 978-0-85769-696-0
Printed in Singapore by Craft Print International

Skills Builders: Grammar and Punctuation

YEAR 5

Contents

* Revision pages

How to use this book

What we have included:

1 Each unit covers aspects of grammar and punctuation taken from the new National Curriculum framework.

2 The units at the beginning of the book focus on basic skills which pupils should recognise from their previous learning and set mini challenges to encourage pupils to recap what they already know. These are often 'Warming up' questions, which are also used to test just learned knowledge throughout the book.

3 Other sections introduce new skills which are organised in a 'Getting hotter' section and some push even further in the 'Burn it up!' section.

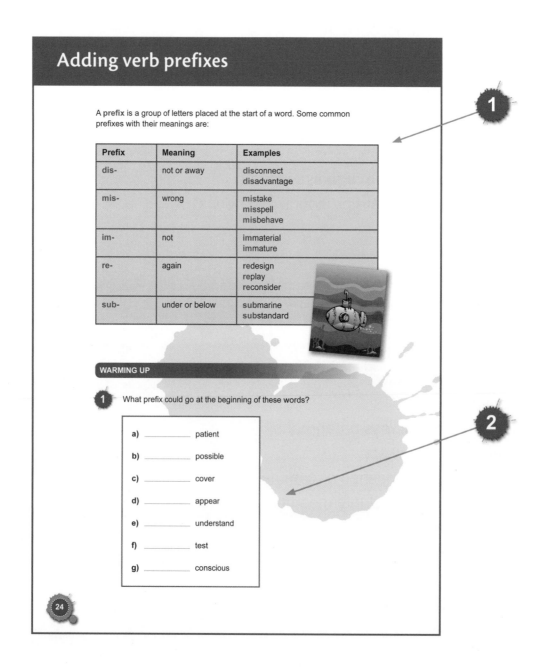

Adding verb prefixes

A prefix is a group of letters placed at the start of a word. Some common prefixes with their meanings are:

Prefix	Meaning	Examples
dis-	not or away	disconnect disadvantage
mis-	wrong	mistake misspell misbehave
im-	not	immaterial immature
re-	again	redesign replay reconsider
sub-	under or below	submarine substandard

WARMING UP

1 What prefix could go at the beginning of these words?

a) _____ patient

b) _____ possible

c) _____ cover

d) _____ appear

e) _____ understand

f) _____ test

g) _____ conscious

24

4

How to use this book

4 At the end of each section is a 'How did I do?' assessment for learning where pupils can record how well they did.

5 There are assessment points throughout the book titled 'Assess and review', which allow opportunities for pupils to recap new learning in small steps.

6 The correct grammatical terminology is used throughout this book to encourage acquisition of technical language.

7 All answers are included so pupils can check on their progress.

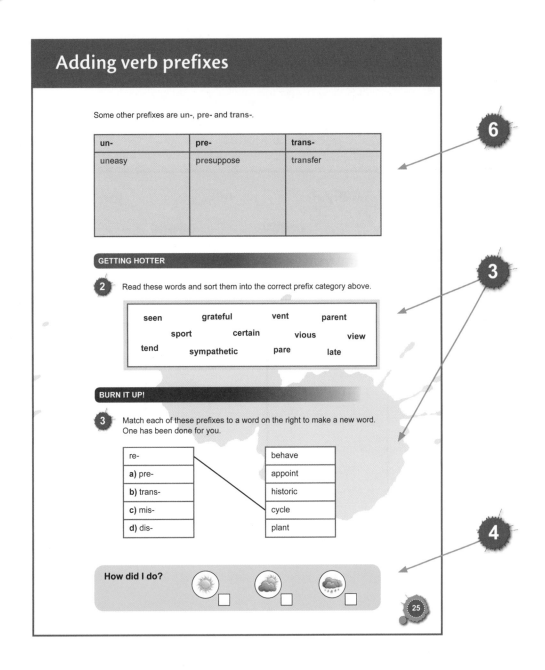

Adding verb prefixes

Some other prefixes are un-, pre- and trans-.

un-	pre-	trans-
uneasy	presuppose	transfer

6

GETTING HOTTER

2 Read these words and sort them into the correct prefix category above.

seen   grateful   vent   parent

sport   certain   vious   view

tend   sympathetic   pare   late

3

BURN IT UP!

3 Match each of these prefixes to a word on the right to make a new word. One has been done for you.

re-		behave
a) pre-		appoint
b) trans-		historic
c) mis-		cycle
d) dis-		plant

How did I do?

4

Word classes

Words are organised into different classes.

Nouns	Adjectives	Verbs	Adverbs
Tell you the names of people, places, feelings and things.	Tell you more about the noun.	Tell you what is happening in the sentence (sometimes referred to as action words).	Tell you the background details – where, how and when events happen.
Tilly Natasha Manchester table love	tallest wealthiest big short smaller	run skipped ate think brought	happily cautiously here inside yesterday

WARMING UP

 1 Sort these words into the correct categories.

> Spain Aaliyah car jog
>
> slowly pretty gentle cute
>
> drank tomorrow play outside

Nouns	Adjectives	Verbs	Adverbs

How did I do?

Punctuation marks

We use full stops, question marks and exclamation marks to end different types of sentences.

.	?	!
Full stop	**Question mark**	**Exclamation mark**
Used to end a statement.	Used to end a question.	Used to end an exclamation or a command.
It is so cold today. I am your best friend. I am in Year 5.	How old are you? Do you need a drink? What is your name?	I don't believe it! Stop! Come here! This is ace! Wow!

WARMING UP

 1 Write these sentences with the correct punctuation.

a) How did you know how to do that ....

b) Give it to me ....

c) Don't you have the box ....

d) I have a cake in my lunch box ....

e) Why did he throw the ball ....

f) Oi, I'm calling you ....

g) I have two pet rabbits ....

h) Wait ....

How did I do?

 ☐   ☐   ☐

Using determiners

A **determiner** goes before a noun and any other words which explain the noun.

These are some of the most common determiners:

> the, a, an, this, my, her, his, your, both, another, neither, either, other, all, those, which, this

In order to vary sentence structure we can change the determiner. For example, if we were writing a paragraph about horses we could begin our sentences in the following ways:

- All horses …
- Some horses …
- Any horse …
- The horse …
- A horse …

WARMING UP

 Complete the following paragraph by inserting appropriate determiners.

_____ school is a place where teachers teach and

children learn. _____ schools are committed to children

making progress. _____ schools have a school uniform

but others do not.

How did I do?

Using prepositional phrases

A **preposition** links a noun or pronoun to another word in the sentence. The preposition usually tells the reader where the object is.

Sometimes prepositional phrases act like **adjectives**. For example:

> The girl **in the park** was laughing.

Sometimes prepositional phrases act like **adverbs**. For example:

> The girl was laughing **in the park**.

When we vary the position of the phrase we are changing our sentence structure.

WARMING UP

 1 Change the word order to create different sentences.

a) The wolf was howling under the bridge.

....

b) The man in the van was shouting.

....

c) The squirrel was hiding nuts up the tree.

....

d) The girl was hopping around the corner.

....

How did I do?   ☐   ☐   ☐

Using apostrophes for contraction

Sometimes we shorten words. When we do this we use an apostrophe to show where letters have been missed out. This is called using an apostrophe for **contraction**.

do not	don't
can not	can't
will not	won't
should have	should've

WARMING UP

1 Complete the table.

I'm	
	could not
I'll	
	is not
	could have
aren't	
they're	
	were not

How did I do?

 ☐   ☐   ☐

Using apostrophes for possession

An apostrophe can also be used to show **possession**.

This means that an apostrophe can be used to show who or what something belongs to. If the owners are plural and end in **-s** (like boys), we add an apostrophe after the **-s**. If the owners are plural but don't end in **-s** (like men), we add an apostrophe followed by an **-s**.

> the girl's pencil = one girl owns one pencil
>
> the girl's pencils = one girl owns more than one pencil
>
> the girls' pencils = more than one girl owns more than one pencil

WARMING UP

 1 Explain each of the following.

the dog's bone = one dog owns one bone

a) the boy's coats = ...

b) the children's pens = ...

c) the man's bag = ...

d) the fairies' wings = ...

e) the policeman's boots = ...

f) the baby's toy = ...

How did I do?   ☐   ☐   ☐

Punctuating direct speech

Direct speech is the exact words used by the speaker or writer. You need to put speech marks or inverted commas around what the speaker says.

"Let me take you to a whole new world," whispered Aladdin to Jasmine.

 1 Some of the punctuation has been stolen from the paragraph below. Rewrite the paragraph so that it is punctuated correctly.

Tilly was shopping with her best friend Natasha when a dazzling ring caught their eyes

Wow exclaimed Tilly Look at that Natasha isn't it beautiful

Natasha moved closer to the diamond ring which displayed the price tag £1,000

Tilly have you seen the price We'd better go to another shop

I suppose you are right Natasha Tilly muttered

As the girls left the jewellery shop they made an agreement that one day they would own a ring just like the one in the window

How did I do?

Using conjunctions

Conjunctions are used to link clauses. Conjunctions can be used for different reasons and can be grouped accordingly.

Co-ordinating conjunctions	Time conjunctions	Causal conjunctions	Conditional conjunctions
Link phrases to create a compound sentence.	Show that time has passed or is passing.	Used in explanations to show cause and effect.	Introduce or link a condition in a sentence.
and but so or	before after until while	since so that because as	although unless if as long as

WARMING UP

 1 Use a conjunction from the table above to complete each sentence.

a) Ben went swimming _____ got home at 7 p.m.

b) Tim brushed his teeth _____ he went to bed.

c) _____ it is raining, we should take our umbrellas with us.

d) _____ it is sunny and warm enough tomorrow, we can go to the beach.

How did I do?

 ☐ ☐ ☐

Fronted adverbials

Fronted adverbials are adverb phrases or clauses which are placed at the beginning of the sentence and usually followed by a comma. They may add more information about time and place. They can also be used to compare or to conclude.

Adverbs of time	Adverbs to compare	Adverbs to conclude
After a while,	On the other hand,	Generally,
Instantly,	Similarly,	In conclusion,
Immediately,	At the same time,	Actually,
Previously,		In fact,

WARMING UP

 1 Match each of the fronted adverbials with a sentence ending to create a new sentence which makes sense.

Immediately, he ran from the forest fire.

Immediately,	the team did play better in the second half.
In conclusion,	Year 5 pupils work extremely hard.
On the other hand,	the summer fair raised a grand total of £500.
Generally,	he ran from the forest fire.

How did I do? ☐ ☐ ☐

Fronted adverbials with commas

Fronted adverbials are

- adverb phrases or clauses which are positioned at the **beginning** of the sentence,

- usually followed by a comma.

For example:

> **During the night,**
> **If I have time,**
> **Since you are so late,**
> **In the city of Paris.**

 1   Read the fronted adverbial, insert the comma and finish each sentence.

a) In August 2012 ....

....

b) In the centre of London ....

....

c) When I was young ....

....

d) As you already know ....

....

e) In Ancient Egypt ....

....

How did I do? ☐   ☐   ☐

Adding -s or -es

When we make regular nouns plural we add **-s**.

cat	+	-s	=	cats
pen	+	-s	=	pens
cake	+	-s	=	cakes

However, if the noun ends with any of the letters in the table, we add **-es**.

s	z	ch	sh	x
glass**es**	buzz**es**	torch**es**	bush**es**	box**es**

There are also some nouns which are irregular and have different endings. For example,

woman	becomes	women,
mouse	becomes	mice,
hoof	becomes	hooves.

WARMING UP

 1 Rewrite each sentence with the underlined noun changed into plural.

a) Hattie put the <u>glass</u> on the table.

....

b) Ravi took his <u>book</u> back to the library.

....

c) Luke played football with his <u>friend</u>.

....

d) Claire took the <u>box</u> upstairs.

....

How did I do?

 ☐   ☐   ☐

Was or were?

Sometimes we confuse **was** and **were** and find it difficult to decide when to use them.

To sort it out we need to learn the **past tense** of the verb to be.

I	was
you	were
he / she / it	was
we	were
you	were
they	were

WARMING UP

 1 Complete the following sentences with was or were.

a) Ten years ago I _____ a baby.

b) How many people _____ at your party?

c) My Mum _____ a nurse when she was younger.

d) The homework _____ easy.

e) It wasn't cold at the park, it _____ warm.

f) The top goal scorer _____ so happy when they won.

g) You _____ supposed to meet me at 6 p.m.!

h) We _____ on holiday last month.

How did I do?

 ☐ ☐ ☐

Using paragraphs to organise ideas

A paragraph needs to be built up accurately. In order to write a detailed paragraph in non-fiction we can apply the **PEE** strategy:

> P: make a point
>
> E: explain your point
>
> E: expand or offer some evidence

For example:

> P: Mobile phones should not be allowed in primary schools.
>
> E: If primary school pupils take their mobile phones to school, it is likely that they may lose them or they could get stolen.
>
> E: Also, if pupils use mobile phones during lessons they will be distracted and will not make progress.

WARMING UP

 1 Choose your own theme and use PEE to write a paragraph.

P ....

....

E ....

....

E ....

....

How did I do?

 ☐   ☐   ☐

18

Choosing appropriate pronouns and nouns

To vary sentences in both fiction and non-fiction texts we can choose **pronouns** to avoid repetition. There are many pronouns which can be used to introduce new ideas, compare ideas and replace nouns.

Re-using the same noun in a sentence often sounds repetitive and awkward.

> **Pritika** loved singing and dancing. **Pritika** entered a talent competition and **Pritika** won. **Pritika** was very proud of **Pritika's** trophy.

We can use pronouns to avoid this.

> **Pritika** loved singing and dancing. **Pritika** entered a talent competition and **she** won. **She** was very proud of **her** trophy.

Here are some pronouns:

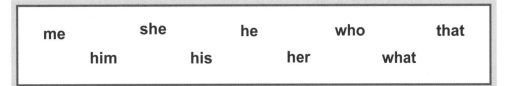

| me | she | he | who | that |
| him | his | her | what | |

WARMING UP

 1 Add a pronoun to complete each of these sentences.

a) Thomas rode _____ bike to school every day.

b) _____ put her shopping bags into the car.

c) My sister told _____ that the rabbit had escaped again.

d) He took a bow at the end of the performance as he knew he had done _____ best.

How did I do?

 ☐   ☐   ☐

Assess and review

WARMING UP

1 Sentences can be statements, questions, exclamations or commands. Read these sentences and label each one either **S** for statement, **Q** for question, **E** for exclamation or **C** for command.

    a) It was just an ordinary day at All Souls' Primary School. ....

    b) What would you like to do this evening? ....

    c) Stop it! ....

    d) This has been the worst day of my life! ....

    e) Do you think it will rain tomorrow? ....

    f) Come here! ....

    g) What a goal! ....

    h) What time does the film start? ....

GETTING HOTTER

2 Write the pair of words that each contraction stands for.

we'd = we would

    a) we're = ...

    b) who's = ...

    c) wasn't = ...

    d) she's = ...

    e) he'll = ...

    f) could've = ...

    g) don't = ...

Assess and review

 3 Read the sentences below and add the apostrophes to show possession.

a) That is Fayes car.

b) The teachers cars were parked in front of the school.

c) The girls coat was on the floor.

d) The policemans hat was blue and white.

e) The babies toys were on the floor.

 4 Rewrite the following sentences using the correct punctuation.

a) "I want sweets, cried the baby."

....

b) Is everything OK?" asked the teacher.

....

c) "I would like to order some foreign currency, said the lady in the post office."

....

....

d) Meet me after school, 3 p.m. sharp, whispered "Tilly to Hattie."

....

....

How did I do?

 ☐   ☐   ☐

Adding suffixes

A **suffix** is a group of letters placed at the end of a word. Knowing suffixes can make spelling easier and increases your vocabulary.

Some rules for spelling when adding suffixes

- For one-syllable words ending with a single vowel and consonant, always double the last consonant before adding a suffix that begins with a vowel. For example, dim**mer**, flat**ten**, slop**py**.

- If the word ends in a double vowel or double consonant, do not double the last consonant. For example, comfort**able**, mind**less**, act**or**.

- If a word ends in 'e', drop the 'e' before adding a suffix that starts with a vowel. For example, tast**ing**, cycl**ed**, rac**er** but not for hope**ful** and home**less**!

WARMING UP

 1 Add the suffixes to these words.

	fright	+	en	=	frighten
a)	strength	+	en	=	_____
b)	moist	+	en	=	_____
c)	weak	+	en	=	_____
d)	soft	+	en	=	_____

Answers

Grammar and Punctuation

YEAR
5

Maddy Barnes

Word classes (page 6)

1 *Nouns:* Spain, Aaliyah, car *Adjectives:* pretty, cute, gentle
  Verbs: drank, play *Adverbs:* outside, tomorrow, slowly

Punctuation marks (page 7)

1 **a)** How did you know how to do that? **b)** Give it to me!
  c) Don't you have the box? **d)** I have a cake in my lunch box.
  e) Why did he throw the ball? **f)** Oi, I'm calling you!
  g) I have two pet rabbits. **h)** Wait!

Using determiners (page 8)

1 **A** school is a place where teachers teach and children learn. **All** schools are committed to children making progress. **Some** schools have a school uniform but others do not.

Using prepositional phrases (page 9)

1 **a)** The wolf under the bridge was howling.
  b) The man was shouting in the van.
  c) The squirrel up the tree was hiding nuts.
  d) The girl around the corner was hopping.

Using apostrophes for contraction (page 10)

1

I'm	I am
couldn't	could not
I'll	I shall / I will
isn't	is not
could've	could have
aren't	are not
they're	they are
weren't	were not

Using apostrophes for possession (page 11)

1 **a)** one boy owns more than one coat
  b) more than one child owns more than one pen
  c) one man owns one bag
  d) more than one fairy owns more than one wing
  e) one policeman owns more than one boot
  f) one baby owns one toy

Punctuating direct speech (page 12)

1 Tilly was shopping with her best friend Natasha when a dazzling ring caught their eyes.

  "Wow!" exclaimed Tilly. "Look at that Natasha, isn't it beautiful?"

  Natasha moved closer to the diamond ring, which displayed the price tag £1,000.

  "Tilly have you seen the price? We'd better go to another shop!"

  "I suppose you are right Natasha," Tilly muttered.

  As the girls left the jewellery shop, they made an agreement that one day they would own a ring just like the one in the window.

Using conjunctions (page 13)

1 **a)** and **b)** before / and **c)** Since / If / As **d)** If

Fronted adverbials (page 14)

1

Immediately,	the team did play better in the second half.
In conclusion,	Year 5 pupils work extremely hard.
On the other hand,	the summer fair raised a grand total of £500.
Generally,	he ran from the forest fire.

Fronted adverbials with commas (page 15)

1 Answers will vary
  a) In August 2012, I watched the Olympics.
  b) In the centre of London, it is always very busy.
  c) When I was young, I liked playing with my sister.
  d) As you already know, the football match is tomorrow.
  e) In Ancient Egypt, there were many slaves.

Adding -s or -es (page 16)

1 **a)** Hattie put the glasses on the table.
  b) Ravi took his books back to the library.
  c) Luke played football with his friends.
  d) Claire took the boxes upstairs.

Was or were? (page 17)

1 **a)** was **b)** were **c)** was **d)** was **e)** was **f)** was **g)** were **h)** were

Using paragraphs to organise ideas (page 18)

1 Answers will vary
  P: Schools are places pupils go to be educated.
  E: All pupils have the opportunity to go to school in the UK.
  E: Throughout British history, schools have not always offered a free education. Instead some schools charged a lot of money so many children did not go to school at all.

Choosing appropriate pronouns and nouns (page 19)

1 **a)** his b) She c) me / him / her d) his

Assess and review (pages 20–21)

1 **a)** S **b)** Q **c)** C **d)** E **e)** Q **f)** C **g)** E **h)** Q
2 **a)** we are **b)** who is **c)** was not **d)** she is **e)** he will **f)** could have
  g) do not
3 **a)** This is Faye's car.
  b) The teachers' cars were parked in front of the school.
  c) The girl's coat was on the floor.
  d) The policeman's hat was blue and white.
  e) The babies' toys were on the floor.

4 a) "I want sweets," cried the baby.

   b) "Is everything OK?" asked the teacher.

   c) "I would like to order some foreign currency," said the lady in the post office.

   d) "Meet me after school, 3 p.m. sharp," whispered Tilly to Hattie.

Adding suffixes (pages 22–23)

1 a) strengthen **b)** moisten **c)** weaken **d)** soften

2 a) gold **b)** bright **c)** smooth **d)** fast **e)** moist **f)** flat

3 careful or careless, fearful or fearless, graceful, effortless or effortful, doubtful or doubtless, bashful, helpless or helpful, harmful or harmless, heartless, hopeless or hopeful

Verb prefixes (pages 24–25)

1 a) impatient **b)** impossible **c)** discover **d)** disappear / reappear

   e) misunderstand **f)** retest **g)** subconscious

2 *un-:* unseen, unsympathetic, ungrateful, uncertain

   pre-: preview, prevent, prepare, pretend, previous

   trans-: transparent, transport, translate

3 a) prehistoric **b)** transplant **c)** misbehave **d)** disappoint

Phrases and clauses (page 27)

1 a) They bought a house which is over 200 years old.

   b) I sent a letter that arrived two weeks late.

   c) The people who live next door are very friendly.

   d) I really love the new restaurant, which we went to last night.

   e) My cousin, who lives with me, loves dogs.

   f) The girl whose doll is lost is very sad.

   g) The summer when I graduated from university was very hot.

   h) Do you know the girl who is wearing a red jacket?

   i) I ate the birthday cake that was on the table.

Using modals (pages 28–29)

1 a) would **b)** Should **c)** might **d)** will **e)** must **f)** can

2 a) must **b)** can't **c)** must **d)** haven't

3 a) must **b)** can't **c)** mustn't **d)** can

4 a) I must look both ways when crossing the street.

   b) I mustn't run in the corridors at school.

   c) I must do my homework.

   d) I mustn't talk during a test.

   e) I must wash my hands before meals.

   (Accept you / your as an alternative to I / my)

Adverbials of probability (pages 30–31)

1 Answers will vary

   a) possibly **b)** probably **c)** definitely **d)** maybe **e)** certainly

   f) definitely **g)** seldom

2 a) never **b)** seldom

3 Answers will vary

   a) Judith is usually very friendly.

   b) They never watch TV in the evening.

   c) The weather is always bad in December.

   d) I sometimes have homework.

e) Is he often angry?

f) She doesn't often travel by taxi.

g) The children always go to the country in the summer.

Assess and review (pages 32–33)

1 a) might / could / will **b)** must / should **c)** must **d)** can't

2 a) appoint **b)** behave **c)** grateful **d)** parent **e)** mature **f)** marine

3 a) that / which **b)** which **c)** that / which **d)** which **e)** who **f)** whose

4 a) certainly **b)** rarely **c)** possibly

Tenses (pages 34–35)

1

Verb	Past	Present	Future
to walk	walked	walk(s)	will walk
to play	played	play(s)	will play
to sing	sang	sing(s)	will sing
to sleep	slept	sleep(s)	will sleep

2 a) He cycled to school. **b)** I drank my coffee with milk.

   c) He cleaned the windows.

3 a) She will sing in the school choir. **b)** The teacher will mark the books.

   c) The baby will walk.

4 a) has melted **b)** have arrested **c)** has written **d)** has been

   e) has hidden **f)** has eaten

Linking ideas across paragraphs (pages 36–37)

1 a) I **b)** C **c)** I **d)** C

2 a) however / but **b)** Finally / Then / After that **c)** therefore / consequently

   d) in addition

Introducing brackets (page 38)

1 a) (her younger brother) **b)** (radius and ulna) **c)** (19th November)

   d) (Hamlet Lane Celtic)

Using brackets, dashes or commas (page 39)

1 Answers will vary: brackets, dashes or commas all acceptable

   a) (Emma Wileman) **b)** (over £10,000) **c)** (in Paris, France)

   d) (who was new to the area) **e)** (which were blue and silver striped)

Using commas to clarify meaning (page 40)

1 a) I washed the dishes, ironed the clothes, cleaned the windows and cut the grass this morning.

   b) The new supermarket, which opens from 8 a.m.–6 p.m., has an underground car park.

   c) Lindsey has travelled all over the world, including Canada, Australia, Korea and China.

   d) Before she knew it, the doors had slammed shut and the candles had blown out.

Double negatives (page 41)

1 a) anything **b)** anywhere **c)** any **d)** anybody **e)** can **f)** any

Informal and formal writing (page 42)

1

	Informal	Formal
a letter to the bank		✓
a postcard to your best friend	✓	
a note to your Mum or Dad	✓	
a letter to the council		✓
a police report		✓

2 a) informal **b)** formal **c)** informal **d)** formal

Assess and review (pages 43–44)

1 a) Amelka is originally from Poland. She loves drawing, painting and craft activities.
   b) The puppies were black and white. They were chasing each other around in the garden.
   c) Eleanor is beautiful and has blonde hair. She has a younger brother called Dylan.

2

Verb	Past	Present	Future
to go	went	go(es)	will go
to take	took	take(s)	will take
to give	gave	give(s)	will give
to begin	began	begin(s)	will begin

3 a) He swims in the sea.
   b) The children eat an apple and an orange for lunch.
   c) She buys a new dress and shoes in town.
   d) Mum paints the door pink and white.

2 Remove the suffix and write the root word (the word that the suffix was originally added to) correctly.

a) golden _____

b) brighten _____

c) smoothen _____

d) fasten _____

e) moisten _____

f) flatten _____

Adding -ful, -ian and -less

	-ful (one l)	-ian	-less
Meaning	full of	person	without
Examples	beautiful	magician beautician technician electrician musician politician	colourless

3 Add the correct suffix to each of the following words.

care   fear   heart

grace   effort   doubt   bash

help   harm   hope

How did I do?

 □   □   □

Adding verb prefixes

A **prefix** is a group of letters placed at the start of a word. Some common prefixes with their meanings are:

Prefix	Meaning	Examples
dis-	not or away	disconnect disadvantage
mis-	wrong	mistake misspell misbehave
im-	not	immaterial immature
re-	again	redesign replay reconsider
sub-	under or below	submarine substandard

1 What prefix could go at the beginning of these words?

a) ....patient

b) ....possible

c) ....cover

d) ....appear

e) ....understand

f) ....test

g) ....conscious

Adding verb prefixes

Some other prefixes are **un-**, **pre-** and **trans-**.

un-	pre-	trans-
uneasy	**pre**suppose	**trans**fer

2 Read these words and sort them into the correct prefix category above.

seen	grateful	vent	parent
sport	certain	vious	view
tend	sympathetic	pare	late

3 Match each of these prefixes to a word on the right to make a new word. One has been done for you.

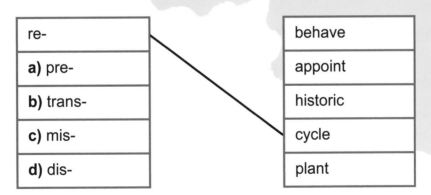

re-	behave
a) pre-	appoint
b) trans-	historic
c) mis-	cycle
d) dis-	plant

How did I do?

25

Phrases and clauses

Here is a summary of the phrases and clauses you are likely to have met so far.

Phrase	A group of words that may have nouns or verbs but does not have a subject doing a verb.	some funny people running up the street
Clause	A group of words that has a subject doing a verb.	because Eleanor likes dancing,
Independent clause	A complete sentence by itself.	Ben went swimming. Thomas eats doughnuts.
Subordinate clause	Starts with a subordinating conjunction and does not make sense by itself.	because Amir likes sport,

Relative clauses

A **relative clause** adds extra information to the sentence by modifying or defining the noun.

The woman who lives next door works at the grocery.

information about the woman

Phrases and clauses

When adding extra information to a sentence we can introduce the relative clause in different ways. For example:

that	who	what	where	which	why

Two sentences = I bought a new car. It is very fast.

One sentence = I bought a new car **that** is very fast.

WARMING UP

 1 Underline the relative clause in the following sentences.

She has a brother <u>who is a doctor</u>.

a) They bought a house which is over 200 years old.

b) I sent a letter that arrived two weeks late.

c) The people who live next door are very friendly.

d) I really love the new restaurant, which we went to last night.

e) My cousin, who lives with me, loves dogs.

f) The girl whose doll is lost is very sad.

g) The summer when I graduated from university was very hot.

h) Do you know the girl who is wearing a red jacket?

i) I ate the birthday cake that was on the table.

How did I do?

 ☐   ☐   ☐

Using modals

The main modal verbs are **will**, **would**, **can**, **could**, **may**, **might**, **shall**, **should**, **must**, **have** and **ought**.

Modal verbs are important for expressing degrees of certainty.

WARMING UP

 1 Underline the modal verb in each sentence.

> **a)** I would like some chocolate ice cream.
>
> **b)** Should I phone you later?
>
> **c)** I might go to New York next year.
>
> **d)** He will score again in this match.
>
> **e)** I must go home and finish my homework.
>
> **f)** He can reach the top shelf now.

GETTING HOTTER

 2 Choose the correct modal to complete each sentence.

> **a)** You've been working all day, you _____ be tired.
> can / must / can't / could
>
> **b)** That sounds ridiculous, it _____ be true.
> must / could / can't / will
>
> **c)** I don't believe it, you _____ be joking!
> could / should / will / must
>
> **d)** I _____ made up my mind yet.
> shouldn't / couldn't / haven't

Using modals

3 Fill in the blanks in these sentences. Choose from:
can   can't   must   mustn't

> **a)** He is ill, he _____ see the doctor.
>
> **b)** I need to have a shower so I _____ come with you to the park.
>
> **c)** You _____ pick flowers in the park.
>
> **d)** I _____ ride my bike by myself now.

4 Decide whether each sentence describes something you must or mustn't do and then rewrite each one as a rule to follow. For example:

Tidy your room.
I must tidy my room.

> **a)** Look both ways when crossing the street.
>
> _____
>
> **b)** Run in the corridors at school.
>
> _____
>
> **c)** Do your homework.
>
> _____
>
> **d)** Talk during a test.
>
> _____
>
> **e)** Wash your hands before meals.
>
> _____

How did I do?   ☐   ☐   ☐

29

Adverbials of probability

We use **adverbials of probability** to show how certain we are about something. Here are some adverbials of probability:

certainly	definitely	maybe	possibly	never
often	sometimes	seldom	probably	always

WARMING UP

 1 Read each statement and choose an adverbial of possibility to match it. For example:

I will grow a tail tomorrow. never

> **a)** It will rain next week ....
>
> **b)** You will watch TV today. ....
>
> **c)** You will eat today. ....
>
> **d)** You will play football tomorrow. ....
>
> **e)** You will brush your teeth today. ....
>
> **f)** You will go to school today. ....
>
> **g)** You will build a snowman this winter. ....

GETTING HOTTER

 2 Some adverbials mean the opposite of another adverbial. Match the opposites.

a) always   possible

b) often   never

impossible   seldom

Adverbials of probability

3 Rewrite each sentence putting the adverbial of probability in the correct place.

He listens to the radio. (**often**)
He **often** listens to the radio.

---

a) Judith is very friendly. (**usually**)

....

b) They watch TV in the evening. (**never**)

....

c) The weather is bad in December. (**always**)

....

d) I have homework. (**sometimes**)

....

e) Is he angry? (**often**)

....

f) She doesn't travel by taxi. (**often**)

....

g) The children go to the country in the summer. (**always**)

....

....

How did I do? ☐ ☐ ☐

Assess and review

1 Add a modal verb to complete each of these sentences.

a) If it is sunny tomorrow I _____ go to the park with Kainaat.

b) My homework is due in tomorrow so I _____ do it tonight.

c) When crossing the road we _____ look both ways.

d) I just _____ stop eating the chocolates!

2 Remove the prefix and write the root word.

recycle   cycle

a) disappoint _____

b) misbehave _____

c) ungrateful _____

d) transparent _____

e) immature _____

f) submarine _____

Assess and review

3 Add **that**, **which**, **who** or **whose** to complete these sentences.

a) I've bought the book _____ you recommended.

b) Our house, _____ is fairly new, has three bedrooms.

c) Was the phone number _____ you gave me correct?

d) Your homework, _____ was very good, is on the table.

e) We saw someone _____ looked like you.

f) The film is a story about a boy _____ parents have left him alone.

4 Match the adverbs of probability which have similar meanings.

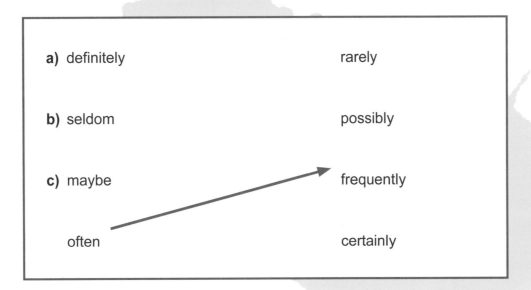

a) definitely   rarely

b) seldom   possibly

c) maybe   frequently

   often   certainly

How did I do?

 ☐   ☐   ☐

33

Tenses

Verbs can be written in the **past**, **present** or **future tense**.

- The **past tense** shows that something has already happened.

- The **present tense** shows that something is happening now.

- The **future tense** shows that something will happen after now.

 1 Complete this table.

Verb	Past	Present	Future
to walk	walked	walk(s)	will walk
to play		play(s)	
to sing	sang		
to sleep			will sleep

2 Rewrite these sentences using the past tense.

a) He cycles to school. ....

b) I drink my coffee with milk. ....

c) He will clean the windows. ....

Tenses

GETTING HOTTER

 3 Change these sentences to the future tense.

> **a)** She sang in the school choir. _____
>
> **b)** The teacher marked the books. _____
>
> **c)** The baby is walking. _____

When we want to write about something that has happened in the past, but we do not specify the time, we use the **present perfect tense**.

> She **has** not **had** her breakfast yet.
> They **have seen** the film already.

BURN IT UP!

 4 Fill in the spaces using the correct form of the verb in the **present perfect tense**.

Alison's flight from Australia has landed. (land)

> **a)** The ice in the park _____ _____ . (**melt**)
>
> **b)** The police _____ _____ three men today. (**arrest**)
>
> **c)** Sundus _____ _____ a letter to her best friend. (**write**)
>
> **d)** It _____ _____ a great week. (**be**)
>
> **e)** My sister _____ _____ in the garden. (**hide**)
>
> **f)** Freddie _____ _____ his lunch. (**eat**)

How did I do? ☐ ☐ ☐

Linking ideas across paragraphs

All good pieces of writing are well organised. This means that there is a clear introduction, paragraphs or sections follow on from each other and there is a conclusion or ending.

Clear introductions engage the reader's attention immediately and punchy endings leave the reader with something to think about.

 1 Read each of the following extracts and decide whether it is an introduction (**I**) or a conclusion (**C**).

a) I am writing this letter to complain about the service we experienced last night at your restaurant.

....

b) As I said earlier, my suggestions for how to spend the gardening budget will benefit everybody.

....

c) Do you find yourself stepping in chewing gum whilst out walking? If you do, you may be interested to read on and discover why the government may ban chewing gum this year.

....

d) I and the rest of the School Council look forward to your response to the above points.

....

Linking ideas across paragraphs

Connectives can be grouped into different types according to their function in the sentence.

To add more information	To offer a contrast	To explain a point	To sequence
in addition	but	because	first
in the same way	however	a result of this	then
furthermore	although	therefore	after that
similarly	in contrast	consequently	finally

GETTING HOTTER

2 Complete each sentence using a connective from the table above.

a) Year 5 were supposed to be going swimming .... the coach did not turn up.

b) .... the race was over and the athletes could relax.

c) "You have not handed your homework in again, ... you have a detention."

d) The service in the restaurant was not good enough. .... to this, the food was also cold.

How did I do?

37

Introducing brackets

Brackets are sometimes called **parentheses** and the information in brackets is called parenthesis.

Brackets show information which is extra to the main text.

Last Friday (the first day of the school holidays) we went swimming.

This is extra information about Friday. The rest of the sentence makes complete sense without the information in brackets.

Dates, dimensions and definitions can also be placed in brackets. As with the first example, the rest of the sentence must also make sense without reading the information in brackets.

World War II (1939–1945) is a significant event in history which the whole world has learnt from.

WARMING UP

 1 Use brackets to punctuate the following sentences.

a) She whispered to Luke her younger brother that she was scared.

b) I broke both bones radius and ulna in my arm.

c) My birthday 19th November is my favourite day of the year.

d) His football team Hamlet Lane Celtic were in the final again.

How did I do?

38

Using brackets, dashes or commas

Parenthesis can be written in **brackets**, between **commas** or between **dashes**.

- Ben Lyons (who lives in Manchester) is an amazing footballer.

- Ben Lyons, who lives in Manchester, is an amazing footballer.

- Ben Lyons – who lives in Manchester – is an amazing footballer.

WARMING UP

 1 Add brackets, dashes or commas to these sentences to enclose the extra information or definitions.

a) Hattie's Mum Emma Wileman is a primary school teacher.

b) The head teacher paid a significant amount of money over £10,000 for new school windows.

c) The Eiffel Tower in Paris, France is 324 m high.

d) The football coach who was new to the area got lost on the way to the match.

e) The trainers which were blue and silver striped were very expensive.

How did I do? ☐ ☐ ☐

39

Using commas to clarify meaning

Commas are really useful punctuation marks because they can help to signal your meaning in your writing.

You must use commas to:

- Separate names, adjectives or items in a list. For example:

  Ben invited Sean, Tim, Lucy and Matthew to the party.

- Separate extra information from the rest of the sentence without affecting its sense. For example:

  Chloe's teacher, Mrs Morris, was really kind and helpful.

- Separate subordinate clauses from a main clause. For example:

  Even though they had saved all of their pocket money, there wasn't enough to pay for their holiday.

WARMING UP

 1 Add commas to punctuate these sentences correctly.

---

a) I washed the dishes ironed the clothes cleaned the windows and cut the grass this morning.

b) The new supermarket which opens from 8 a.m.–6 p.m. has an under ground car park.

c) Lindsey has travelled all over the world including Canada USA Korea and China.

d) Before she knew it the doors had slammed shut and the candles had blown out.

How did I do?

 ☐   ☐   ☐

Double negatives

Double negatives are not used in standard English.

You don't know nothing	=	You don't know anything.
		You know nothing.

Here are some common examples of double negatives:

Non-standard	Standard
She never saw nobody.	She didn't see anybody. She saw nobody.
I'm not helping no more.	I'm not helping any more.
I ain't got none.	I haven't got any.
You're not going nowhere.	You aren't going anywhere. You're going nowhere.

 1   Circle the correct word to complete each sentence.

a) She couldn't eat **anything** / **nothing**.

b) I cannot find my money **anywhere** / **nowhere**.

c) Madison was not carrying **any** / **no parcels**.

d) I did not meet **anybody** / **nobody** at the party.

e) The baby **can** / **cannot** hardly walk yet.

f) Dad could not see **any** / **no** way to help.

How did I do?   ☐   ☐   ☐

Informal and formal writing

Informal writing is personal – features are exclamations, contractions and chatty phrases such as **well**, **like**, **you know**.

Formal writing is impersonal – features are complex sentences and the third person.

WARMING UP

 1 Complete the table by adding a tick to show whether each type of writing should be formal or informal.

	Informal	Formal
a letter to the bank		
a postcard to your best friend		
a note to your Mum or Dad		
a letter to the council		
a police report		

GETTING HOTTER

 2 Add a line to join each sentence to the correct label.

Formal writing

a) You'll never guess what happened next …

b) I cordially invite you to a gathering at my home.

c) Wuu2?

d) I should also like to point out that the refuse bins have not been collected this week.

Informal writing

How did I do?

42

Assess and review

 1 Remove the brackets from these sentences to make two sentences.

Jenny (who was very excited) was waiting to see her favourite pop group.
Jenny was very excited. She was waiting to see her favourite pop group.

a) Amelka (who is originally from Poland) loves drawing, painting and craft activities.

_____

_____

_____

b) The puppies (who were black and white) were chasing each other around in the garden.

_____

_____

_____

c) Eleanor (beautiful with blonde hair) has a younger brother called Dylan.

_____

_____

_____

Assess and review

2 Complete this table for some irregular verbs.

Verb	Past	Present	Future
to go			
to take			
to give			
to begin			

BURN IT UP!

3 Rewrite these sentences in the present tense.

a) He will go swimming in the sea.

_____

b) The children ate an apple and an orange for lunch.

_____

c) She will buy a new dress and shoes in town.

_____

d) Mum painted the door pink and white.

_____

How did I do?

 ☐   ☐   ☐